family feasts

on a budget

money-wise meals,
the Slimming World way

These days we're all trying to make our money go further when we do the weekly shop. At the same time we want to cook deliciously healthy Food Optimised meals that the whole family will enjoy – so we've created this nifty little book to help you shop and slim on a shoestring.

The brilliant thing about Food Optimising is that it's a practical, healthy and tasty way of eating that never leaves you hungry. And because you're cooking your meals from scratch using Free Foods like meat, poultry, fish, vegetables, pasta and rice, you'll get maximum value from your shopping budget. Not only will you spend less, you can be one hundred per cent sure that you and your family are eating fabulously filling food that's full of goodness.

Even the fussiest of eaters will be bowled over by the money-wise dishes we've packed into these pages. As well as home-cooked classics like meatballs, cottage pie and bolognese, you'll find slimmed-down versions of favourites such as chicken tikka and fish & chips, which are easy to make and cost a fraction of a takeout!

All 52 recipes in this book will feed a family of four and, wherever possible, each meal costs under £6 (£1.50 per person)*. And because a bit of savvy shopping really can help you trim your bill, we've also included lots of handy tips on making your money stretch even further – see pages 4-7.

With *Family Feasts on a Budget* in your kitchen you'll keep the whole family satisfied and find yourself saving pounds – on the scales and at the check-out!

happy shopping
and happy slimming!

We've based the cost per serving on prices at a range of popular supermarkets in March 2013, using special offers where available, but prices are subject to change.

feeding your family
on a budget

With food prices rising, we're all feeling the pinch these days. The great news is that it's easy to Food Optimise without breaking the bank – so you can keep your weight loss firmly on track and make sure the whole family stays healthy, happy and well-fed. Our handy tips will help you tighten your belt… in more ways than one!

buying meat, chicken & fish

Meat, chicken and fish are at the heart of many family meals, especially if you're following the Extra Easy or Original eating plans. They can also end up being the priciest items on your shopping list, but there are a few ways you can bring down the cost.

- Inexpensive beef cuts such as chuck steak are ideal in slow-cooked dishes as long as you can remove any visible fat easily. Extra-lean beef mince is affordable and versatile, and it works well in family favourites such as chilli, bolognese and lasagne. If you're not confident about what to buy, make friends with your butcher for advice on cheaper cuts.

- Most families love chicken and the cheapest way to eat it is to buy a whole bird and joint it yourself… however if that sounds like too much hard work, thighs and drumsticks are the most reasonably priced.

- Frozen fish offers better value than fresh fillets, with basa, pollock and coley among the best buys.

- Vegetarian meals can be just as delicious, and cooking without meat once in a while will save you money. Try our chunky bean burgers with Cajun wedges on page 114!

filling your storecupboard

Canned, bottled and dried foods are essential ingredients when you're feeding a family on a budget – they can even make up a meal on their own! Keep your storecupboard stocked with a few everyday basics and you can always rustle up something tasty.

- Staples such as pasta, rice and couscous are ideal for filling hungry tummies. They keep for ages, too, so if you do have space in your cupboards it pays to buy larger bags as they work out much cheaper in the long run.

- Lots of Free and Superfree foods are available canned – eg beans, fish, tomatoes and vegetables – and taste great in hearty pasta dishes and substantial salads. Go for food canned in water or brine rather than oil to avoid adding Syns.

- If you love curries and Asian food and use staples like soy sauce and dried spices, look out for specialist oriental supermarkets, which often have huge packets of spices at a fraction of the cost of supermarket versions.

make friends with the freezer

A freezer is essential when you're short on time and have a hungry family to feed! You can stock up when meat and fish is on special offer and keep a good supply of Superfree frozen vegetables like spinach, broccoli and cauliflower. Your freezer also allows you to cook larger amounts of some recipes and freeze half to serve another day, saving time and money.

Food hygiene experts recommend a few simple safety rules:

- Don't re-freeze anything that has been frozen before, eg if you are using thawed frozen prawns, you shouldn't freeze the leftovers.

- Hot food should be cooled completely before going into the freezer.

- Label frozen food with the contents and the use-by date.

- Defrost frozen meals completely before reheating thoroughly.

at the supermarket

A trip to the supermarket is often the easiest and most convenient way to stock up on all the fresh healthy foods you need for a successful week of Food Optimising. And with a bit of smart shopping, there are plenty of ways to keep your bills low.

Five-a-day!
Fresh, whole Superfree fruit makes a great snack at any time of day and if you keep a variety of fresh vegetables in your kitchen you'll have lots to choose from when you're cooking. Loose veg are usually cheaper than pre-packed or pre-prepared options, while frozen and canned foods are just as healthy but cost less and can be stored for longer. You can save by looking out for what's in season, too – strawberries are cheaper in June than December (as well as being fresher, tastier and better for the environment because they haven't been flown in).

Value brands
If you normally buy well-known brands it's worth trying the supermarket's own-brand or basic ranges – often there's little difference in the flavour, especially with staples like canned tomatoes and dried pasta.

Special offers
We all love a bargain and there are big savings to be made by stocking up on reduced products and those on special promotion such as three-for-two, buy-one-get-one-free and half-price offers (as long as they're ingredients you and your family will be happy to eat and they won't end up at the back of the cupboard!).

Clever swaps
The great thing about Slimming World's recipes is that they're so versatile, you can often substitute ingredients to suit you. For example, if you're planning to make beef burgers and extra-lean pork mince is on offer, make pork burgers instead. The kids will be just as happy!

Compare the market
You might find prices are lower at a different supermarket to the one you usually visit. Although it might take a while to work out where everything is, you could save yourself a small fortune!

Shop savvy
Supermarkets often cut prices after 7pm so shop later in the day to grab the best bargains. If these products are close to their sell-by date, pop them in the freezer until they're needed.

Eat fresh
While cheap ready meals might seem tempting – watch out! The portion sizes are usually small and unsatisfying, and they may be loaded with Syns.

Save those points and be coupon smart!
Loyalty cards reward you with points which you can use towards all sorts of purchases, including money off your shopping bill. Most supermarkets send you coupons to use at the check-out. Keep them in the same place as your loyalty card so you don't forget to use them.

local shops & markets

Bargains galore!
Local shops and markets are a great source of bargains, especially on seasonal fruit and veg, or brands you might not find in the supermarket. Visit near the end of the day for even better value.

It's personal
Another advantage of shopping at local markets, butchers, fishmongers and greengrocers is that staff are eager to help. They can tell you more about what you're buying, give you the exact cut and weight of meat or fish that you need and suggest alternatives.

go online

Easy peasy!
Doing your big shop online is perfect if you like planning your week of healthy Food Optimised meals. Although it's sometimes harder to spot special offers and you can't buy reduced produce, it'll save you time and help avoid expensive impulse buys.

Seven-day menus
Slimming World's website is packed with helpful ideas for eating well on a budget. Check out the helpful seven-day menus on Lifeline Online.

Value for money
We all love a good deal so visit websites like moneysavingexpert.com and mysupermarket.co.uk for up-to-date information on what the supermarkets are offering.

grow your own

If you're lucky enough to have a garden and a little spare time, growing your own veg can save you money and be a very rewarding hobby. Superfree favourites such as carrots and courgettes are reliable growers for beginners, and so are filling potatoes – perfect if your family loves mash or Slimming World chips. If you use a lot of fresh herbs, then a window sill is all you need to grow potted herbs which work out at a fraction of the price of supermarket packets.

using up the leftovers

If your family loved dinner, serving the leftovers the next day will allow everyone to enjoy the same delicious meal all over again. If you're feeling creative, they could also be a starting point for something else: blitz roasted vegetables to make a Superfree soup, mix last night's mash with a tin of tuna to make filling Free fish cakes, or use leftover chicken or beef in a spicy stir-fry.

use your group

You'll find that your Slimming World group is a great source of shopping and cooking tips. Everyone shops at different places so let your group know if you've seen some really good deals – they may well return the favour!

contents

meaty marvels

beef kheema with bombay vegetables	12
beef kofta kebabs with spiced potatoes	14
hearty beef stew	16
best-ever bolognese	18
oven-baked meatballs	20
colcannon cottage pie	22
griddled gammon feast	24
paprika pork	26
saucy chinese pork	28
ham 'n' spud bake	30
cowboy hotpot	32

beef kheema
with bombay vegetables

serves 4

each serving is:

Free on Extra Easy

8 Syns on Green

9 Syns on Original

ready in 30 minutes

❄ up to 3 months,
kheema mince only

low calorie cooking spray

500g extra-lean minced beef

1 large onion, thinly sliced

2 tbsp mild curry powder

400g can chopped tomatoes
with garlic

300ml hot vegetable stock

300g frozen peas

for the bombay vegetables

4 large potatoes, peeled and
cut into chunks

200g Savoy cabbage,
cored and shredded

½ tsp black mustard seeds

½ tsp mild chilli powder

½ tsp turmeric

Every country has its own favourite recipe for mince and India's is kheema. Our tempting version includes beef, onion, peas and a little curry powder, and it's accompanied by subtly spiced Bombay vegetables with a warming hint of chilli – perfect for a curry night and mild enough for the whole family to enjoy!

Spray a large frying pan with low calorie cooking spray, add the mince and fry over a high heat for 4-5 minutes, breaking up the mince with the back of a wooden spoon until browned all over.

Add the onion and curry powder and cook for a further 2 minutes. Stir in the tomatoes, vegetable stock and peas, bring to the boil and simmer for about 15 minutes.

Meanwhile, cook the potatoes in lightly salted boiling water for 5-6 minutes. Add the cabbage and continue to cook for 4 minutes or until the potatoes are just tender. Drain and set aside.

Spray a large frying pan with low calorie cooking spray, then add the mustard seeds, chilli powder and turmeric and cook for 20-30 seconds. Tip in the potato mixture and stir until it is evenly coated with the spices. Cook for 3-4 minutes, stirring until heated through, and serve with the kheema mince.

To make an Indian-style cottage pie with any leftovers (or as an alternative), spoon the mince into an ovenproof dish and top with the mashed Bombay veg mixed with 2 tablespoons of fat free natural fromage frais. Bake at 200°C/Fan 180°C/Gas 6 for 25-30 minutes.

beef kofta kebabs
with spiced potatoes

serves 4

each serving is:

Free on Extra Easy

8 Syns on Green

9½ Syns on Original

ready in 40 minutes

❄ up to 3 months, koftas only

3 medium red onions

500g extra-lean minced beef

1 large red chilli, deseeded and
very finely chopped

4 large garlic cloves, crushed

salt and freshly ground black pepper

1kg charlotte potatoes,
halved lengthways

300g fine green beans

low calorie cooking spray

1 tbsp mild curry powder

400g can chopped tomatoes

Koftas originate from the Middle East and southern Asia and they're an inventive way to make minced beef so much more exotic. Ours are flavoured with chilli and garlic and served with a filling potato salad – they're delicious hot or cold.

Finely chop one red onion and place in a bowl with the beef, chilli (keeping a little to sprinkle when you serve, if you like), half the garlic and some seasoning. Mix well to combine. Divide the mixture into eight equal portions and shape each portion around a metal skewer in a long sausage shape. Chill until ready to cook.

Cook the potatoes in a large pan of lightly salted boiling water for 7-8 minutes. Add the green beans and cook for a further 4 minutes. Drain and set aside.

Meanwhile, spray a large, deep saucepan with low calorie cooking spray. Thinly slice the remaining onions (reserving a small handful to serve) and cook for 4-5 minutes until softened, stirring occasionally. Stir in the remaining garlic and the curry powder and cook for 1-2 minutes. Add the cooked potatoes and beans and the tomatoes and stir well. Cover and simmer for 5-6 minutes until heated through.

Meanwhile, preheat the grill to hot. Arrange the skewers on a foil-lined baking tray and grill for 5 minutes on each side until cooked through. Garnish the skewers with the reserved onion and chilli and serve with the potatoes and green beans.

In the summer, cook these skewers on the barbecue and serve with a salad dressed with mint, cucumber and fat free natural fromage frais.

hearty beef stew

serves 4

each serving is:

Free on Extra Easy

8 Syns on Green

11½ Syns on Original

ready in about 1 hour 40 minutes

❄ up to 4 months

low calorie cooking spray

500g extra-lean stewing steak, all visible fat removed, cut into chunks

1 large onion, finely chopped

2 large carrots, peeled and roughly chopped

2 large parsnips, peeled and roughly chopped

3 large garlic cloves, crushed

2 tsp dried thyme

500ml beef stock

1 tbsp Worcestershire sauce

400g can butter beans, drained and rinsed

4 large potatoes

1 swede

salt and freshly ground black pepper

handful of roughly chopped fresh flat-leaf parsley

Cheaper cuts of beef such as stewing steak need to be cooked for longer to become tender but they can be every bit as delicious as steaks, as this satisfying casserole will prove time and time again.

Preheat the oven to 180°C/Fan 160°C/Gas 4.

Spray a large heavy-based casserole with low calorie cooking spray. Heat gently then brown the beef in batches, setting each batch aside on a plate once it has browned.

Add the onion, carrots, parsnips and garlic to the casserole and cook for 5-6 minutes. Return the meat to the pan, sprinkle over the thyme and pour in the stock and Worcestershire sauce. Bring to the boil, cover and cook in the oven for 1 hour. Stir in the butter beans, then cover and return to the oven for 30 minutes.

Meanwhile, peel the potatoes and swede and cut into chunks. Cook in a pan of lightly salted boiling water for 15 minutes. Drain well and return to the pan over a low heat to drive off any excess moisture. Remove from the heat and crush with the back of a fork. Season to taste and serve with the chunky beef casserole, scattering parsley over the top.

Look out for supermarket value vegetable selection packs, which can work out cheaper than buying vegetables separately. They usually contain onions, carrots, parsnips and swede.

best-ever bolognese

serves 4

each serving is:

Free on Extra Easy

Free on Original

8 Syns on Green

ready in 45 minutes

❄ up to 4 months

low calorie cooking spray

1 large onion, roughly chopped

3 garlic cloves, crushed

½ tsp dried chilli flakes

½ tsp ground cinnamon

1 heaped tsp dried basil

1 large carrot, peeled and finely grated

500g extra-lean minced beef

2 x 400g cans chopped tomatoes

200g passata

1 tsp sweetener

salt and freshly ground black pepper

The classic Italian sauce has never tasted this good! It's fantastic spooned over your favourite pasta with a generous grinding of black pepper.

Spray a large frying pan with low calorie cooking spray and add the onion, garlic and chilli flakes. Cook gently for 4 minutes or until the onion is softened, stirring occasionally.

Add the cinnamon, basil, carrot and beef and fry for 3-4 minutes until browned, stirring occasionally. Add the tomatoes, passata and sweetener. Season, stir well to combine and bring to the boil. Cover and simmer over a low heat for 30 minutes or until thickened.

Serve with your favourite pasta shapes.

Most supermarkets have canned tomatoes in their value ranges and they'll be perfect in this bolognese. A little Parmesan grated over the top is a delicious treat (1½ Syns per level tablespoon).

oven-baked meatballs

serves 4

each serving is:

Free on Extra Easy

Free on Original

8 Syns on Green

ready in about 1 hour 40 minutes

 up to 3 months

2 large onions, finely chopped

500g extra-lean minced beef

2 tsp dried oregano

2 garlic cloves, crushed

salt and freshly ground black pepper

400g can chopped tomatoes

1 tsp sweetener

400g passata with basil

150ml hot vegetable stock

2 medium courgettes, trimmed and cut into chunks

1 medium aubergine, trimmed and cut into chunks

There's an authentic Italian flavour to this mouth-watering dish and shaping the balls with your hands is fun – you might even be able to get the kids to help! It's just like mama used to make!

Preheat the oven to 200°C/Fan 180°C/Gas 6.

Put half the chopped onions in a bowl with the beef, oregano, garlic and some seasoning, then mix well and divide into 20 portions. Roll each portion into a ball and chill until ready to use.

Mix together all the remaining ingredients except the pasta in a large roasting tin and season well. Cover the dish with foil and bake in the oven for 50 minutes. Stir in the meatballs and bake for a further 40 minutes.

Serve with your favourite pasta shapes.

You could make the meatballs using extra-lean turkey mince instead of beef.

colcannon cottage pie

serves 4

each serving is:

Free on Extra Easy

8 Syns on Green

9½ Syns on Original

ready in 1 hour 10 minutes

❄ up to 4 months, unbaked pie only

low calorie cooking spray

1 large onion, finely chopped

2 medium carrots, peeled and finely chopped

3 celery sticks, finely chopped

500g extra-lean minced beef

400g can chopped tomatoes

1 heaped tsp dried oregano

200g passata

splash of Worcestershire sauce

1 tsp sweetener

1 beef stock cube, crumbled

1kg potatoes, peeled and cut into chunks

200g Savoy cabbage, cored and shredded

100g fat free natural fromage frais

salt and freshly ground black pepper

Cottage pie is the ultimate comfort food and a firm favourite with British families. This one features plenty of tasty mince, loads of Superfree vegetables and a topping with a twist – colcannon, the classic Irish recipe for mash with cabbage.

Preheat the oven to 200°C/Fan 180°C/Gas 6.

Spray a large frying pan with low calorie cooking spray. Add the onion, carrots and celery and fry for 5 minutes, stirring occasionally.

Add the beef and cook for 6-7 minutes, stirring continuously, breaking up the meat with the back of a wooden spoon until browned all over.

Stir in the tomatoes, oregano, passata, Worcestershire sauce, sweetener and stock cube. Bring to the boil and simmer for 15 minutes.

Meanwhile, cook the potatoes in a pan of lightly salted boiling water for 15 minutes, steaming the cabbage over the top of the pan for the last 5 minutes or until tender. Drain the potatoes and return to a low heat to drive off any excess moisture. Remove the pan from the heat, stir in the fromage frais and mash until smooth. Season to taste and stir in the cabbage.

Tip the mince into a large ovenproof dish. Spoon the mash on top of the mince and rough up the surface with a fork. Bake for 30 minutes until golden.

For a golden crispy mash topping, cook the pie under a hot grill for the last few minutes. A topping of swede and potatoes is also delicious.

griddled gammon feast

serves 4

each serving is:

Free on Extra Easy

8½ Syns on Original

12 Syns on Green

ready in 35 minutes

4 large baking potatoes

low calorie cooking spray

salt and freshly ground black pepper

4 lean sweetcure smoked gammon steaks, all visible fat removed

2 large tomatoes, deseeded and diced

1 large garlic clove, crushed

3 medium courgettes, trimmed and cut into chunks

4 eggs

small handful of finely chopped fresh flat-leaf parsley

Juicy gammon is a treat for the whole family and it goes perfectly with fried eggs and chunky wedges. It's a weekend fry-up that you can enjoy any night of the week – and it's Free on Extra Easy.

Preheat the oven to 200°C/Fan 180°C/Gas 6.

Line a baking tray with baking parchment. Cut the potatoes lengthways into wedges and arrange in a single layer on the baking tray. Spray with low calorie cooking spray, season and bake for 20-25 minutes until golden and soft.

Meanwhile, heat a griddle until smoking. Spray the gammon steaks with a little low calorie cooking spray and griddle for 3-4 minutes on each side.

While the gammon is cooking, spray a large frying pan with low calorie cooking spray. Add the tomatoes and garlic and sauté for 2-3 minutes over a medium heat. Lift out and set aside. Add the courgettes to the same pan and sauté for 2-3 minutes until golden and softened. Push the courgettes to the side of the pan and break the eggs into the pan, cooking for 2 minutes until the egg white is set. Scatter over the tomato mixture and parsley and season with freshly ground black pepper.

Transfer the gammon steaks to serving plates, top with the eggs and serve with the courgettes and wedges.

Supermarkets sometimes offer good deals on gammon steaks – it's worth buying extra packs to freeze when they do.

paprika pork

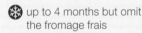

serves 4

each serving is:

Free on Extra Easy

Free on Original

8 Syns on Green

ready in 50 minutes

❄ up to 4 months but omit the fromage frais

low calorie cooking spray

2 large Spanish onions, cut into thin wedges

1 red pepper, deseeded and cut into chunks

500g lean pork fillet, cut into chunks

2 tbsp paprika

300ml chicken or vegetable stock

6 tbsp fat free natural fromage frais

salt and freshly ground black pepper

handful of roughly chopped fresh flat-leaf parsley (optional)

Peppers, onions and paprika add sweetness to the pork in this Spanish-style dish, while the fromage frais adds a lovely creaminess: it's the perfect dish for keeping the cold nights at bay.

Spray a large frying pan with low calorie cooking spray. Add the onions and pepper and cook for 5-6 minutes, stirring occasionally. Stir in the pork and cook for 4 minutes or until browned. Sprinkle over the paprika and cook for 1 minute. Add the stock to the pan and bring to the boil, then cover with a tight-fitting lid and simmer for 30 minutes.

Stir most of the fromage frais into the pork mixture and heat gently for 2 minutes. Season to taste, garnish with the remaining fromage frais and parsley, if using, and serve with boiled rice and Superfree vegetables of your choice.

Pork tenderloin is very lean and the vacuum-packed kind offers the best value.

serves 4

each serving is:

1 Syn on Extra Easy

1 Syn on Original

5½ Syns on Green

ready in about 30 minutes

low calorie cooking spray

1 large red onion, cut into
thin wedges

2 large garlic cloves, crushed

1 large red chilli, halved,
deseeded and thinly sliced

1 tsp ground cumin

2 tsp Chinese five-spice powder

275ml hot vegetable stock

4cm piece of root ginger,
peeled and finely grated

finely grated zest and juice of
1 small orange

1 tbsp soy sauce

2 level tsp cornflour

4 lean pork loin chops,
all visible fat removed

freshly ground black pepper

4 pak choi, trimmed,
leaves separated

600g pack stir-fry vegetables
with bean sprouts

saucy chinese pork

Chinese food is fabulous when you're cooking on a budget as it's packed with big flavours that won't break the bank. This fantastic dish is taken to another level by the mouth-watering combination of ginger, orange, five-spice and chilli.

Spray a saucepan with low calorie cooking spray, add the onion and cook over a high heat for 5 minutes or until softened, stirring occasionally. Add the garlic, chilli, cumin and 1 teaspoon of five-spice powder and cook for 1-2 minutes. Stir in the stock, ginger, orange zest and juice and soy sauce. Bring to the boil and bubble gently for 3 minutes.

Mix the cornflour with 2 tablespoons of cold water to make a smooth paste and add to the saucepan. Cook, stirring, for 2 minutes or until thickened. Keep warm over a very low heat.

Heat a large griddle until smoking. Season the chops on both sides with freshly ground black pepper and the remaining five-spice powder. Spray with a little low calorie cooking spray and cook for 4 minutes on each side or until lightly charred with lines on both sides.

Meanwhile, thinly slice the pak choi stalks. Spray a large wok with low calorie cooking spray and stir-fry the sliced pak choi for 2 minutes, then add the pak choi leaves and stir-fry vegetables and stir-fry for 3-4 minutes. Pour in the sauce and let it bubble for 1 minute.

Serve the pork chops with the stir-fried vegetables.

Every supermarket has its own ready-mixed stir-fry vegetable packs, and the ones including bean sprouts usually offer the best value.

ham 'n' spud bake

serves 4

each serving is:

½ Syn on Extra Easy

4 Syns on Green

17 Syns on Original

ready in about 1 hour

This simple, family-friendly bake is packed with flavour and smothered in a horseradish sauce that gives every plate a touch of luxury.

5 large floury potatoes (such as King Edward), peeled and sliced

3 large sweet potatoes, peeled and sliced

low calorie cooking spray

2 medium red onions, sliced

6 spring onions, trimmed and finely chopped

small handful of fresh thyme leaves

200g lean ham, all visible fat removed

salt and freshly ground black pepper

100g quark

50ml skimmed milk

2 level tsp horseradish sauce

Preheat the oven to 200°C/Fan 180°C/Gas 6.

Cook the potatoes and sweet potatoes in a large pan of lightly salted boiling water for 5 minutes or until just beginning to soften. Drain and set aside.

Spray a large frying pan with low calorie cooking spray, add the red onions and cook for 5 minutes or until softened. Stir in the spring onions and thyme and cook for 2-3 minutes.

Spray a large ovenproof dish with low calorie cooking spray and layer up the potatoes, onion mixture, ham and seasoning, finishing with a layer of potatoes scattered with a little of the onion mixture. Beat together the quark, milk, horseradish and some seasoning until smooth. Pour over the potatoes, cover with foil and bake for 30 minutes. Remove the foil and bake for a further 10 minutes until cooked and golden.

Serve hot with a mixed salad.

Delicatessen counters usually sell ham trimmings – the end bits of ham on the bone that can't be sold as slices. These are great value as long as the visible fat can be removed easily.

cowboy hotpot

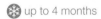

serves 4

each serving is:

1 Syn on Extra Easy

8 Syns on Green

13½ Syns on Original

ready in about 40 minutes

❄ up to 4 months

You don't have to be a cowboy to enjoy this campfire classic!

4 large potatoes, peeled and halved

low calorie cooking spray

1 large onion, roughly chopped

2 garlic cloves, crushed

8 Sainsbury's Be Good To Yourself Extra Lean Cumberland Sausages, each cut into 3 pieces

2 large carrots, peeled and finely diced

150ml hot vegetable stock

400g can chopped tomatoes with herbs

415g can baked beans

410g can mixed beans, drained and rinsed

salt and freshly ground black pepper

Cook the potatoes in a large pan of lightly salted boiling water for 10 minutes or until tender. Drain and set aside.

Meanwhile, spray a deep casserole pan with low calorie cooking spray, add the onion and garlic and cook for 3-4 minutes. Add the sausages and cook for a further 5 minutes, stirring occasionally. Add the carrots, stock and chopped tomatoes. Bring to the boil, cover and simmer for 15 minutes. Stir in the baked beans and mixed beans and cook for a further 5 minutes to heat through.

Preheat the grill to hot.

Spoon the sausages and beans into individual heat-proof serving dishes or a shallow casserole dish. Slice the potatoes and arrange over the top of the sausage mixture. Spray with low calorie cooking spray, season well and grill for 2-3 minutes or until browned.

Serve hot with a mixed salad.

You could also use Tesco Light Choices Reduced Fat Cumberland Pork Sausages in this meal for the same Syns. For a vegetarian version, use Quorn sausages instead (the low fat frozen variety are Free) but keep them whole as they can break down a little on cooking.

poultry perfection

zingy chicken tray bake

serves 4

each serving is:

½ **Syn** on Extra Easy

½ **Syn** on Original

11 **Syns** on Green

ready in about 45 minutes

1 large red onion, cut into
thin wedges

1 butternut squash, peeled,
deseeded and cut into chunks

1 red pepper, deseeded and
cut into chunks

1 yellow pepper, deseeded and
cut into chunks

1 large courgette, trimmed, halved
lengthways and cut into chunks

salt and freshly ground black pepper

3 large garlic cloves, unpeeled

low calorie cooking spray

8 skinless and boneless chicken
thighs, all visible fat removed

1 tbsp all-purpose seasoning

finely grated zest and juice of
1 small lemon

2 level tsp wholegrain mustard

small handful of finely chopped
fresh parsley

Chicken and mustard were made for one another and this low-cost family supper really brings the flavour out of all the Superfree vegetables. Baking everything on one tray is so easy, and makes for much less washing-up!

Preheat the oven to 220°C/Fan 200°C/Gas 7.

Put the onion, squash, peppers and courgette in a large roasting tray and season. Add the garlic cloves and spray with low calorie cooking spray.

Make two cuts into each piece of chicken and rub well with the all-purpose seasoning. Arrange the chicken on top of the vegetables and roast for 25 minutes until golden.

Remove the garlic cloves from the tray and pop the flesh from their papery skins. Mash with a fork and mix with the lemon zest and juice, mustard and parsley. Spoon this sauce over the chicken and vegetables and return the tray to the oven for a further 10 minutes. Serve hot.

Wholegrain mustard adds a lovely flavour to this tray bake but you can make this recipe Free on Extra Easy and Original by using 2 teaspoons of mustard made up with mustard powder and water instead.

serves 4

each serving is:

Free on Extra Easy

Free on Original

8 Syns on Green

ready in about 50 minutes

 up to 3 months

1 tsp cumin seeds

1 tsp coriander seeds

low calorie cooking spray

2 medium onions, finely chopped

4cm piece of root ginger, peeled and finely grated

2 large garlic cloves, crushed

1 tbsp curry powder

1 tsp ground cinnamon

1 tsp paprika

½ tsp ground cardamom

½ tsp turmeric

4 skinless and boneless chicken breasts, all visible fat removed, cut into large pieces

400g can chopped tomatoes

300ml hot chicken stock

400g baby spinach leaves

for the cucumber salad

1 cucumber, trimmed and cut into chunks

4 medium tomatoes, roughly chopped

1 small red onion, thinly sliced

salt and freshly ground black pepper

chicken curry

You won't need to call your family to the table for this satisfying curry – the aroma of warm spices will let them know something delicious is about to be served!

Add the cumin and coriander seeds to a dry frying pan and fry over a high heat for 20-30 seconds until fragrant. Remove from the heat and crush to a fine powder using a pestle and mortar, spice grinder or rolling pin. Set aside.

Spray a large deep saucepan with low calorie cooking spray, add the onions and cook over a low heat for 5-6 minutes, stirring, until softened. Add the cumin and coriander powder, ginger, garlic, curry powder, cinnamon, paprika, cardamom and turmeric and stir-fry for 1-2 minutes.

Add the chicken and cook for 2-3 minutes, stirring continuously so that the spices do not burn and the chicken is sealed. Stir in the chopped tomatoes and stock and bring to the boil. Cover and simmer for 25-30 minutes until thickened.

Meanwhile, make the cucumber salad by mixing together the cucumber, tomatoes and red onion. Season well with salt and freshly ground black pepper.

Stir the spinach into the curry and cook until just wilted. Season to taste and serve with the cucumber salad and boiled rice.

If you can't get hold of ground cardamom, split cardamom pods and crush the tiny black seeds to a fine powder with a pestle and mortar, spice grinder or rolling pin.

BBQ chicken
with apple and dill coleslaw

serves 4

each serving is:

½ **Syn** on Extra Easy

6 Syns on Original

11 Syns on Green

ready in 1 hour 10 minutes,
plus marinating

 up to 4 months

Why wait until summer for a barbecue? All you need is a hot grill, some tasty chicken pieces and our mouth-watering family-friendly marinade. These great-value drumsticks are delicious hot or cold, and the vibrant coleslaw is packed with Superfree fruit and vegetables.

8 chicken drumsticks, skinned

salt and freshly ground black pepper

4cm piece of root ginger, peeled
and finely grated

2 garlic cloves, crushed

2 tbsp barbecue seasoning

2 tbsp soy sauce

2 tbsp white wine vinegar

4 medium baking potatoes

for the coleslaw

1 red apple

finely grated zest and juice
of 1 lemon

½ red cabbage, shredded

1 large carrot, peeled and
cut into matchsticks

small handful of chopped fresh dill

2 level tsp horseradish sauce

6 tbsp fat free natural fromage frais

Make a couple of cuts in each chicken drumstick and season with salt and freshly ground black pepper. In a large dish, mix together the ginger, garlic, barbecue seasoning, soy sauce and vinegar. Add the chicken, stir to coat well, then cover and marinate for 1 hour or overnight if you have time.

Preheat the oven to 200°C/Fan 180°C/Gas 6.

Prick the potatoes all over with a fork and arrange on a baking tray. Season with salt and freshly ground black pepper and bake for about 1 hour.

Line a baking tray with foil and arrange the drumsticks on the foil. Roast underneath the potatoes for the last 30-35 minutes of the cooking time until sticky and cooked through.

While the chicken is cooking, make the coleslaw. Quarter the apple, core, thinly slice and toss in the lemon juice. Drain and place in a bowl with the cabbage, carrot, lemon zest and dill. Mix together the horseradish and fromage frais, season to taste and stir into the coleslaw to coat everything well.

Serve the chicken with the coleslaw and baked potatoes.

Barbecue seasoning adds a delicious summery flavour but if you feel like experimenting you could try other dry-rub spice mixes such as Thai, piri piri or Jamaican jerk.

chicken chasseur

serves 4

each serving is:

2 Syns on Extra Easy

2 Syns on Original

15 Syns on Green

ready in 55 minutes

 up to 3 months

low calorie cooking spray

2 large red onions, thinly sliced

8 skinless and boneless chicken thighs

250g button mushrooms

125ml red wine

1 tsp dried tarragon, plus extra to garnish (optional)

400ml hot chicken stock

400g can chopped tomatoes

1 level tbsp cornflour

salt and freshly ground black pepper

This classic French recipe is the perfect choice when you want to mark a special occasion without splashing out, and the glass of wine makes such a difference to the flavour.

Spray a large, deep frying pan with low calorie cooking spray. Add the onions and stir-fry for 5 minutes or until beginning to soften. Add the chicken and fry for a further 4-5 minutes, turning frequently until it has browned all over and the onions have begun to caramelise. Stir in the button mushrooms, pour over the wine and bubble away for 2-3 minutes.

Add the tarragon, stock and tomatoes. Bring to the boil, cover and simmer gently for about 35 minutes or until the chicken is tender.

Mix the cornflour with 1 tablespoon of water to make a smooth paste, then stir into the chicken mixture until thickened. Season to taste, garnish with tarragon (if using) and serve with Superfree vegetables of your choice.

If you want to save 1 Syn per serving or you're feeding young children, you can replace the wine with an equal amount of chicken stock.

chicken and bacon rösti pots

serves 4

1 Syn on Extra Easy

1 Syn on Original

15½ Syns on Green

ready in about 45 minutes

❄ up to 4 months, filling only

low calorie cooking spray

8 skinless and boneless chicken thighs, cut into chunks

3 lean bacon rashers, all visible fat removed, roughly chopped

1 medium onion, chopped

2 large leeks, trimmed and thinly sliced

small handful of fresh thyme leaves

400ml hot chicken stock

1 level tsp Dijon mustard

½ swede, peeled and coarsely grated

1 egg, lightly beaten

salt and freshly ground black pepper

1 level tbsp cornflour

Individual pies are always a real treat and these taste every bit as good as they look. Cut through a golden swede rösti topping to discover a melting pot of tender chicken, salty bacon and a thick, deeply savoury sauce.

Spray a large frying pan with low calorie cooking spray and fry the chicken and bacon for 5 minutes or until browned. Stir in the onion, leeks and thyme and fry for a further 4-5 minutes, stirring frequently. Pour in the stock and stir in the Dijon mustard. Bring to the boil then turn down the heat, cover and simmer for 25 minutes.

Meanwhile, make the rösti by mixing the grated swede, beaten egg and seasoning together. Spray a large frying pan with low calorie cooking spray and spoon the swede mixture into four piles. Flatten slightly with a fork and cook for 2-3 minutes until golden. Turn over and cook for a further 2 minutes until cooked through and golden.

Mix the cornflour with 2 tablespoons of cold water to form a smooth paste. Pour into the chicken mixture and simmer for 1-2 minutes until thickened. Season to taste with salt and freshly ground black pepper.

Spoon the chicken mixture into individual pie dishes or bowls. Arrange the rösti over the top and serve with Superfree vegetables of your choice.

Rösti are a great way to liven up a meal and you can make them using most hard vegetables – potatoes, parsnips, carrots and sweet potatoes all work well.

chicken tikka skewers with spinach pilau

serves 4

Free on Extra Easy

8 Syns on Green

20 Syns on Original

ready in about 35-40 minutes, plus marinating

150g fat free natural Greek yogurt, plus extra to serve

finely grated zest and juice of 1 lemon

2 tbsp tikka curry powder

2 garlic cloves, crushed

4cm piece of root ginger, peeled and finely grated

salt and freshly ground black pepper

4 skinless and boneless chicken breasts, all visible fat removed, cut into chunks

1 red pepper, deseeded and cut into chunks

2 medium red onions, cut into wedges

8 cherry tomatoes

2 large courgettes, trimmed and sliced

450g dried basmati rice

4 cardamom pods

1 cinnamon stick

¼ tsp turmeric

2 medium carrots, peeled and coarsely grated

175g baby spinach leaves

It's often said that chicken tikka has become one of our national dishes and these tasty skewers are destined to be a favourite with your family.

In a shallow bowl, mix the yogurt, lemon zest and juice, tikka curry powder, garlic and ginger until well combined. Season, add the chicken and stir to coat evenly. Cover and chill for 1 hour or overnight if you have time.

Preheat the grill to hot.

Thread the chicken, pepper, onions, cherry tomatoes and courgettes on to eight metal skewers, arrange on a foil-lined baking tray and grill for about 12 minutes on each side or until browned and cooked through.

Meanwhile, rinse the rice under cold running water until the water runs clear. Tip into a non-stick saucepan and add the cardamom, cinnamon, turmeric, a large pinch of salt, carrots and 600ml of cold water. Bring to the boil, cover and simmer over the lowest heat possible for 10-12 minutes. Very quickly, lift the lid and add the spinach, then cover again and set aside for 5 minutes. Fluff up the rice with a fork – the spinach should have wilted. Remove the cinnamon stick and cardamom pods, if you like.

Serve the skewers immediately with the pilau and extra yogurt sprinkled with a little tikka curry powder.

You can use wooden skewers instead of metal ones but to avoid them burning, soak them in cold water for 30 minutes before using.

crispy chicken cups
with sweet potatoes

serves 4

each serving is:

Free on Extra Easy

7½ Syns on Original

8 Syns on Green

ready in about 50 minutes

4 medium sweet potatoes

low calorie cooking spray

4 skinless and boneless chicken breasts, all visible fat removed, cut into chunks

2 large garlic cloves, crushed

4cm piece of root ginger, peeled and finely grated

2 large carrots, peeled and cut into matchsticks

250g mangetout, shredded lengthways

4 tbsp hot chicken stock

300g bag mixed stir-fry vegetables with bean sprouts

2 tbsp soy sauce

1 iceberg lettuce

Kids will love rolling up these fun lettuce cups, which look stunning and are filled with a fabulous healthy stir-fry. Jacket sweet potatoes are the perfect accompaniment.

Preheat the oven to 200°C/Fan 180°C/Gas 6.

Prick each sweet potato a few times with a fork and place on a foil-lined baking tray. Bake for 45 minutes or until the skin is crispy and the centre is meltingly soft.

Spray a large wok or deep frying pan with low calorie cooking spray and stir-fry the chicken, garlic and ginger over a high heat for 5 minutes or until the chicken is sealed. Add the carrots, mangetout and stock and stir-fry for 4 minutes, then add the stir-fry vegetables and soy sauce and stir-fry for a further 2 minutes.

Pull away eight outer leaves from the lettuce. Divide the hot chicken mixture between the lettuce leaves and roll up to enclose. Serve with the baked sweet potatoes.

If you prefer, you could serve the chicken and vegetables with noodles or rice instead.

garlic and herb
baked chicken

serves 4

each serving is:

Free on Extra Easy

8 Syns on Green

14 Syns on Original

ready in about 35 minutes

Family suppers don't get much simpler or tastier than this. Succulent chicken breasts are stuffed with a delicious garlicky filling and the onions and tomatoes add a cheerful splash of colour.

4 skinless and boneless chicken breasts, all visible fat removed

2 tbsp all-purpose seasoning

1 large garlic clove, crushed

6 tbsp quark

small handful of chopped fresh parsley

low calorie cooking spray

2 red onions, peeled and cut into thin wedges

4 strands of cherry tomatoes on the vine

300g dried bulgar wheat

250g baby spinach leaves

salt and freshly ground black pepper

Preheat the oven to 200°C/Fan 180°C/Gas 6.

Make a lengthways cut in each chicken breast to create a small pocket. Rub the chicken breasts with the all-purpose seasoning.

Mix together the garlic, quark and parsley and use to stuff the pockets in the chicken. Arrange the breasts on a baking tray sprayed with low calorie cooking spray.

Arrange the onions and tomatoes around the chicken and spray with more low calorie cooking spray. Roast for 25 minutes until the chicken is cooked through and the tomatoes have roasted.

Meanwhile, put the bulgar wheat into a saucepan and cover with 1.2 litres of cold water. Bring to the boil, cover and simmer for 12-15 minutes until tender. Drain and stir in the baby spinach leaves, cover with a lid and leave to stand for 5 minutes until the spinach has just wilted. Stir well to combine and season to taste.

Serve the chicken with the tomatoes, onions and bulgar wheat.

Tomatoes on the vine look beautiful on the plate but loose cherry tomatoes work just as well.

turkey burgers with tzatziki

serves 4

each serving is:

Free on Extra Easy

9 Syns on Green

21½ Syns on Original

ready in 25 minutes

❄ up to 3 months, uncooked burgers only

½ small red onion, halved and coarsely grated

500g extra-lean turkey mince

1 tbsp soy sauce

2 tbsp mint sauce, no added sugar

bunch of spring onions, trimmed and finely sliced

500g dried couscous

600ml hot vegetable stock

150g fat free natural Greek yogurt

¼ cucumber, deseeded and diced

salt and freshly ground black pepper

3 large tomatoes, deseeded and roughly chopped

lemon wedges, to serve

Extra-lean turkey mince is great value and tastes fantastic in these light and more-ish burgers. They're delicious served with tzatziki, the classic Mediterranean yogurt dip, and a filling couscous salad.

Preheat the grill to hot.

Put the onion in a bowl with the turkey, soy sauce, 1 tablespoon of mint sauce and half the spring onions. Stir well to combine and shape into four large burgers with your hands.

Arrange the burgers on a foil-lined tray and grill for 6-7 minutes on each side until cooked through.

Meanwhile, place the couscous in a large bowl and pour over the hot stock to just cover. Cover the bowl with cling film and leave to stand for 10 minutes.

While the couscous is soaking, make the tzatziki. Mix together the Greek yogurt, cucumber and remaining mint sauce and season to taste.

Fluff up the couscous with a fork and stir in the tomatoes and remaining spring onions. Season to taste and serve with the burgers, tzatziki and lemon wedges.

Couscous is a handy storecupboard ingredient: try it with leftover roast vegetables such as squash, peppers and aubergine stirred through.

superfree-stuffed
turkey roast

serves 4

each serving is:

Free on Extra Easy

Free on Original

6½ Syns on Green

ready in about 1 hour 15 minutes

Everyone loves sitting down to a lavish family Sunday lunch and it doesn't have to cost a fortune. Our sumptuous turkey breast roast would also make a great choice when you're entertaining friends.

a turkey breast joint, skinned, all visible fat removed (we used 500g)

salt and freshly ground black pepper

low calorie cooking spray

1 medium red onion, finely chopped

2 large garlic cloves, crushed

small handful of fresh thyme leaves

150g chestnut mushrooms, finely chopped

140g baby spinach leaves

300ml hot chicken stock

Preheat the oven to 190°C/Fan 170°C/Gas 5.

Place the turkey breast on a chopping board lined with cling film. Cover the meat with another piece of cling film and bash with a rolling pin or meat mallet to flatten slightly. If necessary, cut a thin slice off the thickest part of the turkey breast and add to the thinnest part to even out the surface. Once flattened, the meat should be about 23cm x 23cm. Season well.

Spray a frying pan with low calorie cooking spray and add the onion, garlic, thyme and mushrooms and cook for 4-5 minutes. Stir in the spinach and cook gently until wilted.

Spread the spinach mixture thinly over the turkey. Roll up tightly like a Swiss roll and tie at intervals with cooking string. Place in a roasting tin and spray with low calorie cooking spray. Pour over the stock and roast for 50 minutes.

Take the turkey out of the oven, remove the cooking string and slice. This is delicious served with mashed potatoes and Superfree vegetables of your choice, with the pan juices spooned over.

deep-sea dining

mediterranean fish roast

serves 4

each serving is:

½ Syn on Extra Easy

7½ Syns on Green

9 Syns on Original

ready in 40 minutes

Roasting Superfree vegetables like courgettes and tomatoes concentrates their delicious flavours and turns them into fantastic partners for tasty fillets of fish. Close your eyes and imagine your family are sitting down to eat in the warm Mediterranean sun!

1kg new potatoes, unpeeled, halved or quartered if large

low calorie cooking spray

1 large red onion, thinly sliced

4 ripe tomatoes, quartered

2 large courgettes, trimmed, halved lengthways and sliced

12 pitted black olives in brine

4 frozen skinless white fish fillets (cod, haddock or basa), thawed

1 lemon

6 tbsp hot fish stock

salt and freshly ground black pepper

small handful of roughly chopped fresh parsley, to garnish (optional)

Preheat the oven to 200°C/Fan 180°C/Gas 6.

Cook the potatoes in a pan of lightly salted boiling water for 10 minutes or until just tender. Drain well and tip into a large roasting tin.

Meanwhile, spray a frying pan with low calorie cooking spray and sauté the onion for 5 minutes or until softened and beginning to colour. Scatter the onion over the potatoes along with the tomatoes, courgettes and olives.

Arrange the fish fillets on top of the vegetables. Cut four slices from the lemon and place one slice on each piece of fish, then squeeze the juice from the remaining lemon over the fish. Pour over the stock, spray with a little low calorie cooking spray and roast for 20 minutes.

Season, scatter the parsley, if using, and serve with your favourite Superfree vegetables.

Many types of fish would be great in this versatile dish. Look for any Free Foods on special offer – salmon, pollock or even smoked haddock would all be just as tasty.

smoked fish florentine stacks

Crisp potato cakes, salty flakes of fresh fish and a golden runny yolk make this beautiful dish a treat for everyone and it's versatile too: try it as a speedy supper, posh brunch or tempting lunch.

4 large King Edward potatoes, peeled

half a bunch of spring onions, trimmed and finely chopped

1 large garlic clove, crushed

salt and freshly ground black pepper

5 eggs

low calorie cooking spray

4 smoked haddock fillets

4 strands of cherry tomatoes on the vine

1 tsp white wine vinegar

250g baby spinach leaves

Preheat the oven to 200°C/Fan 180°C/Gas 6.

Coarsely grate the potatoes and squeeze out as much water as possible using a tea towel. Place the grated potatoes in a bowl and stir in the spring onions, garlic and seasoning. Break in one egg and mix well to combine.

Spray a large frying pan with low calorie cooking spray and place over a medium heat. Divide the potato mixture into four equal portions. Lift two spoonfuls into the frying pan, pressing down with the back of a fork to create two rösti cakes. Cook for 2-3 minutes until golden brown, then turn and cook for a further 2 minutes until golden. Transfer to a plate and keep warm while you fry the remaining two rösti.

Transfer all of the rösti to a baking sheet along with the fish and tomatoes (use a second baking sheet for the fish and tomatoes if there's not enough room). Spray with low calorie cooking spray, season with salt and freshly ground black pepper and bake in the oven for 10-12 minutes.

Bring a pan of water to the boil and add the vinegar. Break the other eggs one at a time and carefully drop each one into the water, poaching for 4 minutes until they are set but the yolks are still soft.

Meanwhile, spray the frying pan with low calorie cooking spray, add the spinach and cook until just wilting.

Divide the rösti between warm plates and top with wilted spinach, the cooked fish and poached eggs. Serve with the cherry tomatoes.

zesty baked fish

serves 4

each serving is:

Free on Extra Easy

Free on Original

7 Syns on Green

ready in 25 minutes

Basa fillets offer fantastic value and their mild flavour means that other ingredients can really shine. Here, we've used creamy quark, spring onions and lemon for a fabulous fresh-tasting family supper – plus a scattering of tasty prawns too!

4 frozen skinless basa fillets, thawed

salt and freshly ground black pepper

4 spring onions, trimmed and finely chopped

4 tbsp quark

finely grated zest and juice of 1 small lemon

small handful of finely chopped fresh parsley

100g frozen jumbo king prawns, thawed

Preheat the oven to 200°C/Fan 180°C/Gas 6 and line a baking tray with baking parchment.

Pat the thawed fish with kitchen paper to remove as much excess water as possible and arrange the fillets on the baking tray. Season with a little salt and pepper.

Mix the spring onions, quark, lemon zest, parsley and prawns and season to taste with lemon juice (about 1 tablespoon) and salt and pepper. Spread the quark mixture lightly over the fish fillets and bake for 15 minutes.

This fish dish is delicious served with new potatoes and Superfree vegetables of your choice.

The creamy quark and prawn mixture in this recipe would also make a great filling for a steaming hot baked potato.

fisherman's pie

serves 4

each serving is:

1½ Syns on Extra Easy

8 Syns on Green

12½ Syns on Original

ready in 1 hour

1kg floury potatoes, peeled and cut into chunks

100g fat free natural fromage frais

salt and freshly ground black pepper

low calorie cooking spray

1 large leek, trimmed and thinly sliced

2 level tbsp wholemeal plain flour

300ml hot fish stock

4 frozen Alaskan pollock portions, thawed, each fillet cut into 4 equal pieces

300g bag frozen seafood selection, thawed

175g frozen peas, thawed

This ever-popular supper is filled with all the goodness of the ocean and makes fantastic comfort food on a cold night. Feel free to change the fish to whatever your family likes best or what you find on special offer.

Preheat the oven to 200°C/Fan 180°C/Gas 6.

Cook the potatoes in a large pan of lightly salted boiling water for 12-15 minutes or until tender. Drain well and return to the heat to drive off any excess moisture. Add the fromage frais and mash well. Season to taste and set aside.

Spray a large frying pan with low calorie cooking spray, add the leek and fry over a low heat for 5 minutes or until softened, stirring occasionally. Sprinkle over the flour and stir to coat well. Gradually add the fish stock and simmer for 3 minutes until the sauce has thickened, stirring continuously. (The sauce will seem quite thick at this stage but this allows for any juices from the fish to loosen it while the pie is baking.) Season to taste.

Pat the fish dry with kitchen paper to remove any excess water. Add the pollock, seafood and peas to the sauce and stir well to coat. Spoon into a large ovenproof dish, cover with the mashed potato and bake for 40 minutes or until golden brown.

Serve hot with Superfree vegetables or your choice.

Leftover herbs such as parsley or dill would be lovely in this pie – chop them finely and add them with the fish just before baking.

salt 'n' pepper fish fingers with chips and tartare sauce

serves 4

each serving is:

3½ Syns on Extra Easy

10½ Syns on Green

12 Syns on Original

ready in 40 minutes

The most popular words in the English language may well be 'fish and chips'. And with Slimming World you don't have to miss out on the classic family takeaway – our healthy and totally more-ish fish finger version is every bit as satisfying.

4 frozen skinned white fish fillets such as cod, haddock or basa, thawed

2 tsp all-purpose seasoning

2 tsp coarse ground black pepper

125g wholemeal bread, crumbed

salt

1 egg, lightly beaten

4 large baking potatoes

low calorie cooking spray

lemon wedges, to serve

for the tartare sauce

200g fat free natural fromage frais

2 spring onions, trimmed and finely chopped

4 tbsp capers, drained and rinsed

4 gherkins, finely chopped

large handful of chopped fresh flat-leaf parsley

Preheat the oven to 200°C/Fan 180°C/Gas 6 and line two baking trays with baking parchment.

Pat the fish fillets dry with kitchen paper and cut each fillet into thick strips. In a bowl, mix together the all-purpose seasoning, black pepper, breadcrumbs and a little salt. One by one, dip each fish finger into the beaten egg, coat evenly in the breadcrumbs and arrange on one of the baking trays. Chill for 15 minutes.

Meanwhile, cut the potatoes into chips, leaving the skins on if you like them that way. Arrange in a single layer on the other baking tray, spray with low calorie cooking spray and season with a little salt and pepper. Place the chips on the top shelf of the oven and bake for 10 minutes. Place the tray of fish on the middle shelf of the oven and bake both trays for a further 15 minutes or until golden.

Mix the tartare sauce ingredients, season to taste and chill until ready to serve.

Serve the fish fingers with the chips, tartare sauce and lemon wedges. This is delicious with a large mixed salad.

All-purpose seasoning is a blend of salt, coriander, paprika, chillies, garlic, onion and celery. It adds a delightful savouriness to the fish and is available in most large supermarkets.

tandoori fish with saag aloo

serves 4

each serving is:

Free on Extra Easy

7 Syns on Green

8½ Syns on Original

ready in 35 minutes, plus marinating

6 tbsp fat free natural Greek yogurt

1 tbsp tandoori masala curry powder or other curry powder

2 large garlic cloves, crushed

finely grated zest and juice of 1 small lemon, plus wedges to serve

salt and freshly ground black pepper

4 frozen skinned white fish fillets such as cod, haddock, coley or basa, thawed

900g potatoes, peeled and cut into chunks

low calorie cooking spray

2 tsp cumin seeds

1 tsp ground coriander

½ tsp hot chilli powder

½ tsp garam masala

100g baby spinach leaves

150g cherry tomatoes, halved

Tandoori food takes its name from the tandoor – a traditional Asian clay oven – but all you need to create these amazing flavours at home is your trusty grill! Saag aloo is a fantastic side dish of spiced potato and spinach which goes perfectly with the fish.

In a shallow bowl, mix together the yogurt, curry powder, garlic, lemon zest, 1 tablespoon of lemon juice and some seasoning. Add the fish and turn to coat. Cover with cling film and marinate for 30 minutes or longer if you have time.

Meanwhile, cook the potatoes in a pan of lightly salted boiling water for 10 minutes or until just tender. Drain well and tip on to a baking tray, spreading them out so that they dry out a little.

Spray a large frying pan with low calorie cooking spray, add the cumin seeds and cook over a high heat until fragrant. Remove the pan from the heat and spray with a little more low calorie cooking spray. Return the pan to a low heat, add the potatoes and cook for 8 minutes or until the potatoes are lightly browned and golden.

Preheat the grill to hot. Arrange the fish on a foil-lined baking sheet and grill for 12 minutes.

Sprinkle the remaining spices over the potatoes and cook for a few minutes, stirring carefully to coat well. Add the spinach and the tomatoes to the potatoes, turn the heat to high and cook until the spinach has just wilted.

Season the potatoes to taste and serve immediately with the grilled fish and lemon wedges.

Tandoori masala powder gives a rich red colour to the fish and is available from most large supermarkets. If you can't find any, curry powder will work just as well.

baked fish cakes with dill sauce

225g skinned salmon fillet, thawed if frozen

225g skinned coley fillet, thawed if frozen

finely grated zest and juice of 1 small lemon, plus wedges to serve

2 large baking potatoes, peeled and cut into chunks

half a bunch of spring onions, trimmed and finely chopped

175g frozen peas, thawed

1 level tbsp horseradish sauce

small handful of chopped fresh dill

salt and freshly ground black pepper

low calorie cooking spray

1 egg, lightly beaten

for the dill sauce

2 level tsp cornflour

5 tbsp skimmed milk

5 tbsp hot vegetable stock

2 tbsp freshly squeezed lemon juice

small handful of chopped fresh dill

These filling cakes are packed with fish and potato and infused with the refreshing flavours of lemon and dill plus a gentle kick of horseradish. We predict they'll be a big hit with adults and children alike!

Preheat the oven to 200°C/Fan 180°C/Gas 6.

Arrange the fish on a large piece of baking parchment and drizzle with 2 tablespoons of lemon juice. Wrap the fish in the parchment, place on a baking tray and bake for 12 minutes or until just cooked.

Meanwhile, cook the potatoes in a pan of lightly salted boiling water for 12-15 minutes or until tender. Drain and return the potatoes to a low heat to drive off any excess moisture, then remove from the heat and mash.

Stir the spring onions, peas, horseradish sauce, lemon zest and dill into the mash and season to taste. Tip the fish into the mash and stir through gently to break the fish into flakes.

Increase the oven temperature to 220°C/Fan 200°C/Gas 7.

Spray a large baking sheet with low calorie cooking spray. Divide the fish mixture into eight equal portions and shape them into cakes. Arrange the cakes on the prepared tray, then brush with beaten egg and bake for 20 minutes or until golden.

While the fish cakes are baking, make the sauce. Blend the cornflour with a little of the milk to make a smooth paste, then stir in the remaining milk and the stock and pour into a small saucepan. Heat gently, stirring until thickened. Season to taste, stir in the lemon juice and dill and simmer for 1-2 minutes.

Divide the fish cakes between plates, spoon over the sauce and serve with lemon wedges and Superfree vegetables of your choice.

For a special occasion, stir 150g of peeled prawns into the sauce and heat through gently for 1-2 minutes before spooning over the fish cakes.

spiced mackerel
with stir-fried vegetables

serves 4

each serving is:

Free on Extra Easy

Free on Original

22 Syns on Green

ready in 30 minutes

Mackerel is rich in omega-3 fatty acids, which are thought to be important for a healthy heart. It's also very reasonably priced, making it a great budget option for families.

4 whole mackerel, heads removed, gutted and cleaned

low calorie cooking spray

salt and freshly ground black pepper

2 garlic cloves, thinly sliced

2 large red chillies, deseeded and cut into thin strips

2 small lemons

1 small red onion, halved and thinly sliced

½ tsp mustard seeds

for the stir-fried vegetables

2 tsp fennel seeds

2 tsp cumin seeds

1 large red pepper, deseeded and thinly sliced

1 small red onion, halved and thinly sliced

350g Savoy cabbage, finely shredded

½ tsp mild chilli powder

½ tsp garam masala

Preheat the oven to 200°C/Fan 180°C/Gas 6.

Make two or three cuts on each side of the mackerel and arrange on a baking tray sprayed with low calorie cooking spray. Season the fish inside and out and rub with the garlic and chillies. Slice one of the lemons and place the slices inside the fish cavities along with the red onion slices.

Finely grate the zest from the remaining lemon and squeeze out the juice, adding the husks to the baking tray. Spray a large frying pan with low calorie cooking spray, add the mustard seeds and fry over a high heat until they start popping. Add the lemon zest and juice and cook for 1-2 minutes, then pour over the fish and bake for 15 minutes.

Meanwhile, make the stir-fried vegetables. Wipe the frying pan with kitchen paper and spray with low calorie cooking spray. Add the fennel seeds and cumin seeds and fry over a high heat for 30 seconds. Turn down the heat, add the pepper and most of the onion and stir-fry for 5 minutes or until softened. Add the cabbage and stir-fry for 4-5 minutes. Sprinkle over the chilli powder and garam masala and stir-fry for a further 2 minutes.

Garnish the mackerel with the remaining onion and serve with the stir-fried vegetables.

To get the most juice out of a lemon or lime, pop it in the microwave and heat for 10 seconds to warm up slightly. Alternatively, roll it in your hands.

pasta, rice
and all things nice

tuna and salsa pasta

serves 4

each serving is:

Free on Extra Easy

3 Syns on Green

22 Syns on Original

ready in 20 minutes,
plus 30 minutes' marinating

finely grated zest and juice
of 1 small lemon

1 tbsp white wine vinegar

½ small red onion, finely chopped

4 large ripe vine tomatoes,
roughly chopped

2 x 160g cans tuna in spring water,
drained and flaked

small handful of roughly chopped
fresh flat-leaf parsley

2 tbsp capers, drained and rinsed

salt and freshly ground black pepper

500g dried fusilli or other dried
pasta shapes

300g fine green beans, trimmed

Fresh salsa dances on the tongue and turns this easy pasta dish into something special. It's great served hot or cold, and any leftovers would make a great lunch the next day tossed with crisp green salad leaves.

Put the lemon zest and juice, vinegar and red onion into a bowl and leave for 30 minutes to remove the bitterness from the onion (it's time well spent!).

Add the tomatoes, tuna, parsley and capers to the onion and toss well. Season and set aside.

Cook the pasta according to the packet instructions, adding the green beans 5 minutes before the end of the cooking time. Drain, reserving 50ml of the cooking liquid.

Return the pasta to the warm pan and toss with the reserved cooking liquid and tuna salsa mixture. Serve hot or cold.

If you don't have time to marinate the red onion you can use four thinly sliced spring onions instead. Add them to the tuna mixture along with the lemon zest, juice and vinegar.

linguine with crab, chilli, lemon and rocket

serves 4

each serving is:

Free on Extra Easy

2½ Syns on Green

22 Syns on Original

ready in 20 minutes

Tinned crab is a great alternative to fresh crab and makes a handy storecupboard standby. Add the zing of lemon and the bite of chilli and you have an easy supper your family will ask for again and again.

500g dried linguine pasta

low calorie cooking spray

4 spring onions, trimmed and thinly sliced

1 garlic clove, crushed

1 large red chilli, deseeded and thinly sliced

2 x 170g cans white crabmeat, drained

finely grated zest and juice of 1 lemon

4 plum tomatoes, deseeded and cut into thin wedges

small bag of rocket leaves

freshly ground black pepper

Cook the pasta according to the packet instructions. Drain, reserving 50ml of the cooking liquid, and set aside.

Spray the warm saucepan with low calorie cooking spray. Add the spring onions, garlic and chilli and cook over a low heat for 2-3 minutes until softened, stirring often. Stir in the crab, lemon zest, tomatoes and the reserved cooking liquid and heat gently.

Return the pasta to the saucepan along with the rocket and toss well to combine. Season with freshly ground black pepper and squeeze over a little fresh lemon juice to taste. This is best eaten straight away – forks to the ready!

If you have the storage space in your kitchen, it's worth picking up a jumbo bag of pasta – there are big savings to be made from buying in bulk.

sausage and mustard pasta

serves 4

each serving is:

1½ Syns on Extra Easy

8½ Syns on Green

16½ Syns on Original

ready in 20 minutes

350g penne or other dried pasta shapes

8 Sainsbury's Be Good To Yourself Extra Lean Cumberland Sausages

low calorie cooking spray

1 large red onion, cut into thin wedges

50ml hot chicken or vegetable stock

250g fat free natural fromage frais

1 tbsp wholegrain mustard

salt and freshly ground black pepper

200g baby spinach leaves

Sausage and mustard go together brilliantly and this simple recipe shows off the partnership at its very best. Fromage frais adds an appealing creaminess to a dish that will keep the whole family satisfied.

Cook the pasta according to the packet instructions then drain and set aside, reserving 50ml of the cooking liquid.

Meanwhile, remove and discard the sausage skins and snip each sausage into four equal pieces. Spray a large frying pan with low calorie cooking spray, add the sausage pieces and onion and fry over a high heat, stirring occasionally, until the sausages are crisp and cooked through. Tip on to a plate and cover with a bowl to keep warm.

Add the stock, fromage frais, mustard and reserved cooking liquid to the pasta saucepan and heat gently (too high a heat and the fromage frais will curdle). Season to taste with salt and freshly ground black pepper.

Remove the pan from the heat, stir in the spinach and leave until just wilted. Add the pasta and sausages, stir well to combine and heat gently until piping hot. Serve hot with a crispy vegetable salad.

You could use Tesco Light Choices Reduced Fat Cumberland Pork Sausages for the same Syns. For a cheesy twist, scatter Parmesan over this dish before serving (1½ Syns per level tablespoon).

sweet potato pasta bake

serves 4

each serving is:

1 Syn on Extra Easy

1 Syn on Green

19 Syns on Original

ready in 45 minutes

350g dried macaroni

1 head broccoli, trimmed and cut into small florets

1 large sweet potato, peeled and cut into small chunks

300g low fat natural cottage cheese

small handful of finely chopped fresh chives

2 eggs, beaten

4 tbsp quark

150g cherry tomatoes, halved

30g reduced fat Cheddar cheese, grated

Pasta bakes are always a great option for family food because they're easy to make, tasty and extremely satisfying. This one features a lovely cheesy sauce plus plenty of healthy sweet potato, tomato and broccoli.

Preheat the oven to 200°C/Fan 180°C/Gas 6.

Cook the pasta according to the packet instructions, adding the broccoli and sweet potato 4 minutes before the end of the cooking time.

Meanwhile, mix together the cottage cheese, chives, eggs and quark and stir well.

Drain the pasta, stir in the cottage cheese mixture and tomatoes and tip the pasta into an ovenproof dish. Scatter over the Cheddar cheese and bake for 20-25 minutes until golden.

This dish is equally delicious made with roasted vegetables such as peppers, onions, butternut squash or courgettes – stir them into the cooked pasta before baking in the oven.

creamy mushroom and prawn pasta

low calorie cooking spray

350g mixed mushrooms, halved, sliced or trimmed

2 large garlic cloves, crushed

salt and freshly ground black pepper

250g baby spinach leaves

225g frozen jumbo king prawns, thawed

150g fat free natural fromage frais

Long pasta is perfect with this tasty recipe. We recommend pappardelle – which takes its name from the Italian word pappare, meaning 'to gobble up' – but your family will be just as keen on spaghetti or tagliatelle!

Spray a large frying pan with low calorie cooking spray. Add the mushrooms and garlic and cook over a high heat for 3-4 minutes. Season to taste.

Stir in the spinach and prawns and cook until the spinach has wilted and the prawns are cooked through. Remove from the heat, add the fromage frais and a couple of tablespoons of hot water, and stir until smooth.

Spoon the prawn mixture over your favourite pasta to serve.

Loose mushrooms are much cheaper than the pre-packed kind and you'll save money by buying them from the greengrocer.

leek, pea and ham farfalle

serves 4

each serving is:

1 Syn on Extra Easy

4 Syns on Green

18 Syns on Original

ready in 20 minutes

350g dried farfalle pasta

175g frozen peas

low calorie cooking spray

2 leeks, trimmed and thinly sliced

150ml hot chicken or vegetable stock

100g fat free natural fromage frais

2 large eggs, lightly beaten

175g lean ham, all visible fat removed, shredded

30g reduced fat Cheddar cheese, grated

salt and freshly ground black pepper

The word farfalle comes from the Italian for butterfly, although many people think these pretty pasta shapes look like little bow ties! Whatever your view, there's no doubt that this is a simple and very satisfying supper – kids will love the tasty ham and cheese.

Cook the pasta according to the packet instructions, adding the frozen peas for the last 3 minutes of the cooking time.

Meanwhile, spray a large frying pan with low calorie cooking spray and fry the leeks for 2-3 minutes. Pour in the stock and simmer for 4-5 minutes. Remove from the heat and stir in the fromage frais.

Drain the pasta and peas and return to the pan. Quickly stir in the eggs, leek mixture, ham and Cheddar and cook for 1-2 minutes, stirring well.

Season to taste and serve with a mixed salad.

You'll save money by buying loose leeks from the greengrocer rather than washed and cleaned leeks in supermarket packs.

roasted chicken and pepper pasta

serves 4

each serving is:

Free on Extra Easy

Free on Original

8 Syns on Green

ready in 40 minutes

❄ up to 3 months

low calorie cooking spray

1 large red onion, cut into thin wedges

1 red pepper, deseeded and cut into strips

1 yellow pepper, deseeded and cut into strips

1 green pepper, deseeded and cut into strips

2 garlic cloves, crushed

leaves of 1 rosemary sprig, finely chopped

300ml hot vegetable stock

400g can chopped tomatoes

salt and freshly ground black pepper

4 cooked skinless and boneless chicken breasts, roughly shredded

This simple dish is so easy to make and it looks beautiful thanks to the vibrant colours of the peppers. If you have any chicken left over from a roast, you could use it here instead of buying more.

Spray a large frying pan with low calorie cooking spray and fry the onion, peppers, garlic and rosemary for 4-5 minutes until softened. Pour in the stock and tomatoes. Season with salt and freshly ground black pepper, bring to the boil and simmer for 30 minutes.

Add the chicken to the pepper sauce for the last 5 minutes of the cooking time to heat through.

Serve hot with your favourite pasta shapes.

Look out for supermarket value multi-bags of peppers, which are significantly cheaper than buying loose peppers. Don't worry if they only contain red and green peppers – these will taste just as good.

chunky italian vegetable pasta

serves 4

each serving is:

Free on Extra Easy

Free on Green

Free on Original

ready in 40 minutes

❄ up to 3 months

This classic sauce is packed with healthy Superfree vegetables and it's so easy to make. Any leftovers would be lovely spooned into baked potatoes or served with grilled fish, meat or chicken.

low calorie cooking spray

1 large red onion, cut into wedges

3 garlic cloves, crushed

2 large carrots, peeled and diced

2 large fennel bulbs, trimmed and cut into chunks

2 medium courgettes, trimmed and cut into chunks

400g can cherry tomatoes

400g passata

150ml hot vegetable stock

large handful of fresh basil leaves

1 tsp sweetener

Spray a large saucepan with low calorie cooking spray and place over a low heat. Add the onion, garlic, carrots, fennel and courgettes and fry for 3-4 minutes.

Add the tomatoes, passata, stock, most of the basil leaves and the sweetener. Bring to the boil and simmer for 20-25 minutes, stirring occasionally, until the sauce has thickened and the vegetables are tender.

Garnish the vegetables with the remaining basil and serve with pasta shapes of your choice.

This fantastic sauce is so versatile – it's worth making double amounts and putting half into your freezer for a rainy day.

creamy pasta sauce

serves 4

each serving is:

1½ Syns on Extra Easy

1½ Syns on Green

1½ Syns on Original

ready in 10 minutes

2 level tsp cornflour

150ml skimmed milk

150ml vegetable stock

250g fat free natural fromage frais

1 level tsp Dijon mustard

salt and freshly ground black pepper

large handful of chopped mixed fresh herbs, such as chives, parsley, tarragon, chervil or basil (optional)

This simple and luxurious sauce is great with pasta but it can be used in many other ways too: try it as a white sauce for bakes or as a sauce to spoon over meat.

Blend the cornflour with a little of the milk to make a smooth, thick paste. Stir in the remaining milk and the stock, pour into a saucepan and heat very gently for 2-3 minutes, stirring until warmed through and just thickened.

Remove the sauce from the heat and stir in the fromage frais and Dijon mustard. Season to taste and stir in the herbs, if using.

Serve with your favourite pasta and Superfree vegetables.

If you'd like to try this sauce with meat, you could swap the mustard for 1 level teaspoon of horseradish sauce.

pasticcio

serves 4

each serving is:

1½ Syns on Extra Easy

9½ Syns on Green

16½ Syns on Original

ready in 1 hour

low calorie cooking spray

1 large onion, roughly chopped

3 garlic cloves, crushed

½ tsp dried chilli flakes

½ tsp ground cinnamon

1 large carrot, peeled
and finely grated

500g extra-lean minced beef

2 x 400g cans chopped tomatoes

200g passata

1 tsp sweetener

salt and freshly ground black pepper

350g dried rigatoni pasta

for the white sauce

2 level tsp cornflour

150ml skimmed milk

150ml vegetable stock

150g fat free natural fromage frais

1 level tsp Dijon mustard

small handful of finely chopped
fresh parsley

If you haven't heard of this tempting Greek recipe before, imagine a cross between family favourites moussaka and lasagne. The rich and tasty beef mince has hints of chilli and cinnamon, and it's topped with a filling layer of baked creamy pasta.

Spray a large frying pan with low calorie cooking spray. Add the onion, garlic and chilli flakes and heat gently for 4 minutes until the onion is softened, stirring occasionally.

Add the cinnamon, carrot and beef and stir-fry for 3-4 minutes until browned. Add the canned tomatoes, passata and sweetener. Season and stir to combine. Bring to the boil, cover and simmer over a low heat for 25-30 minutes until thickened. Pour into a large ovenproof dish.

Meanwhile, cook the pasta according to the packet instructions, then drain and set aside.

Preheat the oven to 200°C/Fan 180°C/Gas 6.

Make the white sauce. Blend the cornflour with a little of the milk to make a smooth, thick paste. Stir in the remaining milk and the stock, pour into a saucepan and heat gently for 2-3 minutes until warmed and thickened. Remove from the heat and stir in the fromage frais, mustard and parsley. Season to taste and stir into the pasta to coat evenly. Spread the pasta over the meat in the dish and bake for 20 minutes.

Serve with your favourite Superfree vegetables.

*For a veggie option you can
replace the beef with minced Quorn.*

chilli prawn stir-fry

serves 4

each serving is:

Free on Extra Easy

2 Syns on Green

10 Syns on Original

ready in 20 minutes

225g dried rice vermicelli noodles

low calorie cooking spray

2 large garlic cloves, crushed

4cm piece of root ginger, peeled and finely grated

1 large red chilli, deseeded and cut into thin strips

1 tbsp mild curry powder

150ml vegetable stock

bunch of spring onions, trimmed and thinly sliced

1 tbsp freshly squeezed lime juice

300g bag mixed stir-fry vegetables

2 pak choi, trimmed, leaves separated and stalks thinly sliced

225g frozen jumbo king prawns, thawed

½ tsp chilli flakes

Prawns add a touch of luxury to this super stir-fry, which is packed with exciting flavours. This recipe is mildly spiced but if your family prefers it hot you could double the amount of chilli!

Soak or cook the noodles according to the packet instructions. Drain well and set aside.

Spray a wok or large frying pan with low calorie cooking spray. Add the garlic, ginger and fresh chilli and fry over a low heat for 2-3 minutes until softened.

Sprinkle over the curry powder and cook for 1 minute, stirring, then pour in the stock and add the spring onions and lime juice. Simmer for 3-4 minutes then pour into a measuring jug and wipe the wok with kitchen paper.

Spray the wok with more low calorie cooking spray and cook the stir-fry vegetables and pak choi stalks over a high heat for 3 minutes. Add the pak choi leaves, prawns, chilli flakes and noodles, then pour in the sauce and stir-fry for another 2-3 minutes. Serve hot.

If your family don't like the vegetables in the mixed stir-fry packs, prepare their favourites instead.

sweet and sour chicken noodles

serves 4

each serving is:

2½ Syns on Extra Easy

10½ Syns on Green

13½ Syns on Original

ready in about 30 minutes

low calorie cooking spray

4 skinless and boneless chicken breasts, all visible fat removed, roughly sliced

200ml hot chicken stock

1 tbsp tomato purée

2 tbsp white wine vinegar

3 tbsp dark soy sauce

1 level tbsp cornflour

300g fresh pineapple, peeled, cored and cut into small pieces

250g dried egg noodles

1 large red onion, cut into thin wedges

1 large red pepper, deseeded and cut into thin strips

1 large yellow pepper, deseeded and cut into thin strips

2 large carrots, peeled and cut into matchsticks

2 large garlic cloves, crushed

300g bag stir-fry vegetables with bean sprouts

The whole family can enjoy our sensational home-cooked version of the classic Chinese takeaway at a fraction of the cost. And you can rest assured you're keeping your weight loss perfectly on track, as our lighter version has all the flavour with the bare minimum of the Syns.

Spray a large wok or deep frying pan with low calorie cooking spray and stir-fry the chicken over a high heat for 5 minutes or until lightly coloured. Transfer the chicken to a bowl with a slotted spoon and cover to keep warm.

In a small saucepan, gently heat the stock, purée, vinegar and soy sauce. Mix the cornflour with 2 tablespoons of water to make a smooth paste and stir into the sauce. Heat gently, stirring until thickened, then add the pineapple. Set aside and cover to keep warm.

Cook the noodles according to the packet instructions then drain and set aside.

Meanwhile, wipe the wok with kitchen paper and spray with low calorie cooking spray. Add the onion and peppers and stir-fry for 3-4 minutes, then add the carrots, garlic and stir-fry vegetables and stir-fry for another 2 minutes.

Return the chicken to the wok along with the noodles. Pour in the sauce and stir-fry for 2-3 minutes until piping hot. Serve straight away.

If your family loves chicken, look out for multi-buy bags of individual breasts, as these can often work out cheaper than buying packs of two or four breasts.

singapore noodles

serves 4

each serving is:

Free on Extra Easy

5 Syns on Green

12 Syns on Original

ready in 25 minutes

250g dried medium egg noodles

low calorie cooking spray

1 large onion, cut into thin wedges

2 red chillies, deseeded and thinly sliced

225g lean pork tenderloin fillet, cut into thin strips

2 garlic cloves, crushed

4cm piece of root ginger, peeled and finely grated

1 tbsp medium curry powder

1 tsp turmeric

bunch of spring onions, trimmed and roughly sliced

300g pack mixed stir-fry vegetables with bean sprouts

2 tbsp soy sauce

150ml chicken or vegetable stock

100g frozen peas, thawed

175g frozen jumbo king prawns, thawed

This ever-popular curried noodle dish goes down a storm as a midweek family supper. You'll need to buy a whole pork tenderloin and halve it, so wrap the other half in cling film and freeze to use at a later date. We think you'll end up using it to make this amazing stir-fry again!

Prepare the noodles according to the packet instructions, then drain and set aside.

Spray a large wok with low calorie cooking spray. Add the onion and cook over a high heat for 2-3 minutes. Add the chillies, pork, garlic, ginger, curry powder and turmeric and stir-fry for 5 minutes or until the pork is cooked through. Tip on to a plate and cover with a bowl to keep warm.

Wipe the wok with kitchen paper and spray with low calorie cooking spray. Add the spring onions and stir-fry vegetables and cook over a high heat for 2 minutes. Stir in the remaining ingredients and return the pork mixture and noodles to the wok, then stir-fry for 2-3 minutes over a high heat until the ingredients are well combined and piping hot. This is best served straight away.

This is a very flexible dish – swap the pork for skinless chicken breast, turkey escalopes or lean beef steak if you fancy a change.

nasi goreng

serves 4

each serving is:

Free on Extra Easy

8 Syns on Green

13 Syns on Original

ready in 20 minutes

300g dried long-grain rice

salt and freshly ground black pepper

300g small broccoli florets

low calorie cooking spray

4 skinless and boneless chicken breasts, cut into thin strips

2 tbsp medium curry powder

1 large onion, thinly sliced

3 garlic cloves, crushed

5cm piece of root ginger, peeled and finely grated

2 red chillies, deseeded and thinly sliced

300g bag mixed stir-fry vegetables

2 tbsp soy sauce

This traditional Indonesian dish translates as 'fried rice'. We've used chicken, broccoli and mixed stir-fry vegetables but it's an ideal recipe for using up whatever spare meat or vegetables you have to hand.

Cook the rice according to the packet instructions, then drain and set aside.

Meanwhile, blanch the broccoli in boiling water for 2 minutes. Drain and set aside.

Spray a large wok with low calorie cooking spray and add the chicken, curry powder and onion. Cook for 3-4 minutes over a medium heat until the chicken begins to colour. Add the garlic, ginger, chillies, broccoli, stir-fry vegetables and 3-4 tablespoons of water, then cover and cook for 2-3 minutes, shaking the pan occasionally. Remove the lid and stir well.

Fluff up the rice with a fork and add to the wok with the soy sauce. Stir-fry for 2-3 minutes until cooked through, then season to taste and serve hot.

If you feel like replacing the stir-fry vegetables with vegetables of your choice, cut them into even-sized pieces so that they take the same time to cook (harder vegetables such as carrots need 1-2 minutes longer in the pan).

fragrant
spiced biryani

serves 4

each serving is:

Free on Extra Easy

Free on Green

14 Syns on Original

ready in 35 minutes,
plus soaking

Delicious, aromatic basmati is the ideal rice for this
classic Indian dish, which is packed full of fragrant
spices and fresh Free and Superfree vegetables.
You won't be able to resist second helpings!

250g dried basmati rice

low calorie cooking spray

1 large onion, roughly chopped

2 garlic cloves, crushed

4cm piece of root ginger, peeled
and finely grated

1 level tsp ground cumin

1 level tsp ground coriander

1 level tsp mild chilli powder

½ tsp lightly crushed
cardamom pods

1 large carrot, peeled and diced

1 large sweet potato, peeled
and diced

1 courgette, trimmed and diced

400g small cauliflower florets

½ tsp turmeric

salt and freshly ground black pepper

300g fine green beans

Place the rice in a bowl, pour over enough cold water to cover and leave
to soak for 20 minutes. Tip the rice into a sieve and run under cold running
water until the water runs clear.

Meanwhile, spray low calorie cooking spray into a deep, heavy-based
casserole pan that has a tight-fitting lid. Put the pan over a medium heat,
add the onion and sauté for 5 minutes until softened and beginning to
brown. Add the garlic and ginger and cook for 1 minute, stirring continuously.

Add the cumin, coriander, chilli and cardamom and cook for 2-3 minutes,
stirring, so that the spices don't stick to the bottom of the pan. Add the
carrot, sweet potato, courgette, cauliflower and 300ml of water and bring
to the boil. Cover and simmer for 5 minutes.

Drain the rice and add to the casserole along with 250ml of boiling water
and the turmeric. Stir well and season with a little salt and freshly ground
black pepper. Bring to the boil, cover and cook over the lowest possible
heat for 12-15 minutes, without lifting the lid.

About 5 minutes before the end of the cooking time, cook the green
beans in a pan of lightly salted boiling water until tender. Drain well.

Fluff up the rice, stir in the green beans and serve hot.

*Biryani is also delicious with meat and chicken
leftovers. Slice, dice or chop the meat or chicken into
chunks and add to the pan along with the rice.*

ginger and prawn fried rice

serves 4

each serving is:

Free on Extra Easy

2 Syns on Green

15 Syns on Original

ready in 20 minutes

300g dried long-grain rice

low calorie cooking spray

1 large onion, chopped

2 garlic cloves, crushed

4cm piece of root ginger, peeled and finely grated

2 large red chillies, deseeded and thinly sliced

2 large carrots, peeled and cut into matchsticks

175g frozen peas

1 large red pepper, deseeded and cut into thin strips

6 tbsp hot vegetable stock

225g frozen jumbo king prawns, thawed

bunch of spring onions, trimmed, half shredded and half finely sliced

2 tbsp soy sauce

2 eggs, lightly beaten

Fresh ginger costs very little but makes a big difference to the flavour of Asian food. It really packs a punch in this fabulous stir-fry, even giving the prawns a run for their money as the star of the show!

Cook the rice according to the packet instructions, then drain and set aside.

Meanwhile, spray a large non-stick wok with low calorie cooking spray and add the onion, garlic, ginger and chillies and stir-fry for 2-3 minutes. Add the carrots, peas, pepper and stock and simmer for 5-6 minutes, stirring occasionally.

Add the prawns, cooked rice, shredded spring onions and soy sauce and stir-fry for 1-2 minutes to heat through. Push the rice mixture to one side of the wok, add the eggs and cook until set. Stir the eggs through the rice and serve hot, garnished with the sliced spring onions.

Fresh chillies add an appealing heat to this dish but dried chilli flakes will make it just as tasty – it's worth keeping a jar in your storecupboard.

kedgeree

300g dried basmati rice

1 tsp cumin seeds, lightly crushed

1 tsp fennel seeds, lightly crushed

low calorie cooking spray

1 medium onion, finely chopped

2 garlic cloves, crushed

4cm piece of root ginger, peeled and finely grated

2 tsp medium curry powder

1 large carrot, peeled and diced

150ml hot vegetable stock

150g frozen peas

salt

450g frozen smoked haddock, thawed and skinned

4 large eggs

fresh coriander sprigs, to garnish (optional)

This versatile Anglo-Indian breakfast, brunch or supper dish is thought to have its roots in an ancient Indian rice and lentil dish called khichri but it was the British who came up with the idea of adding fish and eggs. One thing's for sure: it's a sensational combination of colours and flavours!

Place the rice in a bowl, pour over enough cold water to cover and leave it to soak for 20 minutes. Tip the rice into a sieve and run under cold water until the water is clear.

Put the cumin seeds and fennel seeds into a large, non-stick lidded pan and heat gently for 30-40 seconds until fragrant. Tip into a bowl and set aside.

Spray the pan with low calorie cooking spray, add the onion, garlic and ginger and cook over a low heat for 3-4 minutes, stirring occasionally. Add the cumin seeds, fennel seeds, curry powder and carrot and cook for 1-2 minutes. Stir in the stock and bubble for 5 minutes or until the carrots are just tender.

Stir in the peas and soaked rice. Pour in 600ml of cold water, season with a little salt and lay the fish over the top. Bring to the boil, then cover, turn the heat down to very low and cook for 12 minutes, without lifting the lid.

Meanwhile, place the eggs into a pan of cold water, bring to the boil and bubble for 5 minutes or until cooked to your liking. Drain and run under cold running water until cool enough to handle, then peel and halve the eggs.

Fluff up the rice with a fork, breaking the fish into flakes. Serve with two egg halves on each plate and garnish with coriander, if you like.

Frozen smoked fish usually has a distinctive bright yellow colour. If you prefer, you can buy undyed fresh smoked haddock instead.

viva veg

serves 4

each serving is:

Free on Extra Easy

Free on Green

14 Syns on Original

ready in 45 minutes

 up to 3 months

2 large onions, chopped

2 large garlic cloves, crushed

4cm piece of root ginger, peeled and finely grated

1 large red chilli, deseeded and chopped

½ tsp coarse ground black pepper

2 tsp ground cinnamon

2 tsp turmeric

2 tsp ground coriander

2 tsp ground cumin

low calorie cooking spray

2 x 400g cans chopped tomatoes

175g dried red split lentils

175g dried yellow split lentils

1 medium cauliflower, trimmed and broken into florets

200g baby spinach leaves

2 tsp garam masala

salt and freshly ground black pepper

cauliflower
dhansak

This delicious and filling meat-free curry puts Superfree cauliflower and spinach in the spotlight. This dish is lightly spiced so if you want more heat, double the amount of chillies.

Put the onions, garlic, ginger, chilli and 8 tablespoons of cold water into a food processor with the pepper, cinnamon, turmeric, coriander and cumin and whizz to make as smooth a paste as you can.

Spray a large deep saucepan with low calorie cooking spray and fry the paste for 5-6 minutes, stirring occasionally. Add one can of chopped tomatoes, the lentils and 1 litre of cold water. Bring to the boil, cover and simmer gently for 30 minutes until thickened and the lentils are soft.

About 10 minutes before the end of the cooking time, cook the cauliflower in a pan of lightly salted boiling water until just tender. Drain well and carefully stir into the lentils with the remaining tomatoes, spinach and garam masala. Heat gently to warm through, season to taste and serve.

Lentils are very filling and make a great storecupboard staple. Dried lentils are better value but canned lentils are quicker to use as they only need to be heated through. If you're using canned lentils here, drain and rinse, then add for the last 5 minutes of cooking.

chunky bean burgers
with cajun wedges

serves 4

each serving is:

Free on Extra Easy

Free on Green

14 Syns on Original

ready in 45 minutes

❄ up to 1 month

Ⓥ

400g can haricot or cannellini beans, drained

400g can kidney beans, drained

1 small onion or shallot, roughly chopped

1 large garlic clove, crushed

1 red chilli, deseeded and roughly chopped

1 small red pepper, deseeded and roughly chopped

bunch of spring onions, trimmed and roughly chopped

salt and freshly ground black pepper

1 egg, beaten

low calorie cooking spray

4 large baking potatoes

2 tsp Cajun seasoning

6 tbsp fat free natural Greek yogurt

2 large tomatoes, roughly chopped

Burgers for supper means smiles all round and the whole family will love these bean-packed veggie versions. We've served them with tempting Cajun wedges and a refreshing chunky sauce.

Place the beans, onion, garlic, chilli, red pepper and half the spring onions into a food processor and whizz to chop roughly. Transfer to a bowl, season to taste and stir in the beaten egg. Divide the mixture into eight equal portions and shape into burgers. Place on a baking tray sprayed lightly with low calorie cooking spray and chill for 20 minutes.

Preheat the oven to 200°C/Fan 180°C/Gas 6.

Cut the potatoes into wedges and toss with the Cajun seasoning, then arrange on a baking tray, spray with low calorie cooking spray and bake for 25 minutes or until golden.

When the wedges have been cooking for about 10 minutes, put the burgers on the oven shelf below the wedges and bake for 12-15 minutes or until golden.

Meanwhile, mix the yogurt, tomatoes and remaining spring onions in a bowl and season to taste.

Serve the bean burgers with the wedges, chunky sauce and your favourite Superfree salad.

Cajun seasoning is a ready-mixed blend of cumin, coriander, paprika, salt, pepper and oregano but, if you can't find it, a sprinkling of salt, pepper and mild chilli powder will make your wedges taste fantastic.

tex-mex veggie chilli
with chilli cream

serves 4

each serving is:

Free on Extra Easy

Free on Green

3 Syns on Original

ready in 40 minutes

 up to 4 months

3 large red chillies

low calorie cooking spray

1 large onion, roughly chopped

2 large garlic cloves

1 red pepper, deseeded and cut into chunks

1 orange pepper, deseeded and cut into chunks

2 tsp ground cumin

1 tsp ground cinnamon

1 tsp paprika

500g Quorn mince

400g can chopped tomatoes with chilli and garlic

500g passata with herbs

400g can kidney beans, drained

6 tbsp fat free natural fromage frais

Chilli is a very big deal in the southern states of the US and our mildly hot veggie version is as mouth-watering as anything you'll taste over there. Our amazing chilli cream is the ideal accompaniment and will get everyone talking!

Deseed and finely chop two of the red chillies. Spray a large, deep saucepan with low calorie cooking spray and add the chopped chillies, onion, garlic and peppers. Fry over a medium heat for 5 minutes or until softened, stirring occasionally. Sprinkle over the cumin, cinnamon and paprika and cook for 1-2 minutes, stirring well.

Stir in the Quorn mince, tomatoes, passata, kidney beans and 300ml of cold water. Bring to the boil, cover and simmer for 20 minutes.

Meanwhile, use long-handled tongs to cook the remaining chilli directly over an open flame, carefully turning until charred. Place the chilli into a plastic food bag, seal and leave to steam for 10 minutes. Remove the chilli's blackened skin and seeds. Using the blade of a knife, mash the chilli flesh and stir into the fromage frais.

Serve the chilli with the chilli cream and boiled rice.

If you don't have a gas hob or you don't want to cook the chillies over an open flame, you can roast them in an oven preheated to 200°C/Fan 180°C/Gas 6 for 10 minutes then steam in a bag as above.

quottage pie

serves 4

each serving is:

Free on Extra Easy

Free on Green

10½ Syns on Original

ready in 55 minutes

❄ up to 4 months

🅥 if you omit the Worcestershire sauce

low calorie cooking spray

2 large onions, chopped

2 celery sticks, trimmed and finely chopped

2 large carrots, peeled and diced

500g Quorn mince

400g can chopped tomatoes with garlic and herbs

1 tbsp Worcestershire sauce (optional)

300ml hot vegetable stock

salt and freshly ground black pepper

415g can baked beans

750g new potatoes, unpeeled and scrubbed

Our Quorn-based version of cottage pie will be a hit with vegetarians and everyone else too – in fact you might not be able to tell the difference between this and a meaty version!

Preheat the oven to 200°C/Fan 180°C/Gas 6.

Spray a large, deep frying pan with low calorie cooking spray. Add the onions, celery and carrots and stir-fry for 4-5 minutes. Stir in the Quorn, tomatoes, Worcestershire sauce (if using) and stock. Bring to the boil, cover and simmer for 20 minutes. Season to taste and stir in the baked beans.

Meanwhile, cook the potatoes in a pan of lightly salted boiling water for 15 minutes until tender. Drain well and roughly crush with the back of a fork.

Tip the Quorn mince mixture into a large ovenproof dish, spoon over the potatoes to cover and bake for 20-25 minutes until golden.

Serve hot with Superfree vegetables of your choice.

The crushed new potatoes give a wonderful texture to the topping and make it extra hearty but, if you prefer, you can use traditional mash mixed with fat free natural fromage frais or even mashed root vegetables.

squash and mushroom filo pots

serves 4

each serving is:

2 Syns on Extra Easy

2 Syns on Green

2 Syns on Original

ready in 1 hour 10 minutes

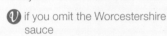 if you omit the Worcestershire sauce

low calorie cooking spray

1 small butternut squash, peeled, deseeded and cut into chunks

small handful of fresh thyme leaves

3 large garlic cloves, crushed

1 large red onion, cut into thin wedges

salt and freshly ground black pepper

250g chestnut mushrooms, sliced

2 level tsp cornflour

200ml vegetable stock

1 tbsp Worcestershire sauce (optional)

100g baby spinach leaves

1 large sheet filo pastry, quartered

These stunning individual filo-topped pies will make everyone feel a little bit special and the fabulous filling of Superfree vegetables will satisfy the biggest appetites, too.

Preheat the oven to 200°C/Fan 180°C/Gas 6.

Spray a large roasting tray with low calorie cooking spray and add the squash, thyme, garlic and red onion. Season and roast for 40 minutes or until softened, shaking the pan a few times during cooking. Leave the oven on when they're done.

Meanwhile, spray a large frying pan with low calorie cooking spray and fry the mushrooms over a high heat for 4-5 minutes.

Mix the cornflour with 2 tablespoons of water to make a smooth paste and stir into the vegetable stock. Add the Worcestershire sauce (if using) and pour over the mushrooms. Cook for 1-2 minutes until thickened slightly. Add half the spinach and stir until wilted, then add the remaining spinach and stir until wilted. Add the roasted vegetables and stir to mix well, then spoon the mixture into four individual pie dishes.

Scrunch each piece of filo pastry and use to just cover each of the pies. Arrange the pie dishes on a baking tray and spray with low calorie cooking spray. Season with salt and freshly ground black pepper and bake for 12-15 minutes until crisp and golden.

These are delicious served with new potatoes and Superfree vegetables of your choice.

Filo pastry is delicious but it dries out very quickly. The best way to keep it fresh is to cover it with a damp cloth while you prepare your pies.

serves 4

each serving is:

Free on Extra Easy

Free on Green

25 Syns on Original

ready in 55 minutes

❄ up to 3 months

Ⓥ

low calorie cooking spray

1 large red onion, cut into wedges

1 large garlic clove, crushed

4cm piece of root ginger, peeled and finely grated

2 tsp ground cumin

2 tsp ground coriander

1 tsp ground cinnamon

1 tsp turmeric

1 tsp dried chilli flakes

2 x 400g cans chopped tomatoes

1 litre hot vegetable stock

1 tsp sweetener

1 butternut squash, deseeded, peeled and cut into chunks

400g can chickpeas, drained

1 red pepper, deseeded and cut into chunks

500g dried couscous

seeds of 1 pomegranate (optional)

large handful of roughly chopped fresh mint

salt and freshly ground black pepper

moroccan vegetable tagine

Tagines are irresistible rich stews from North Africa and our vegetarian version features sweet, satisfying squash and healthy chickpeas, with a side dish of couscous that you can stud with crunchy pink pomegranate seeds.

Spray a large deep saucepan with low calorie cooking spray. Add the red onion, garlic and ginger and fry over a medium heat for 3-4 minutes, stirring. Add the dry spices, tomatoes, 450ml of the stock and sweetener and bring to the boil.

Add the butternut squash, cover and simmer for 30 minutes. Add the chickpeas and red pepper and simmer for a further 10-15 minutes until the squash is tender.

Meanwhile, place the couscous into a bowl and pour over the remaining stock until just covered. Cover and leave for 5 minutes or until all the stock has been absorbed. Fluff up with a fork, stir in the pomegranate seeds – if you are using them – plus most of the mint and season well.

Garnish the tagine with the remaining mint and serve with the couscous.

If you have any tagine left over, it can be blitzed with water to make a delicious lightly spiced soup.

index

notes

First published in 2013 by
Slimming World
Clover Nook Road
Somercotes
Alfreton
Derbyshire
DE55 4SW
UK
www.slimmingworld.com

Created and designed by
Slimming World's publications team.
Publications manager: Allison Brentnall
Editor: Oliver Maxey
Designer: Fabiana Viracca-Butler
Syn calculation: Beverley Farnsworth

Recipes and food styling: Lorna Brash
Photographs: Karen Thomas
Styling: Morag Farquhar
Front cover photograph: Leek, pea and ham farfalle, pg 86